The Emperor and the
Peasant Boy

by Rosa Martinez
illustrated by Steve Sanford

Harcourt

Orlando   Boston   Dallas   Chicago   San Diego

Visit *The Learning Site!*

www.harcourtschool.com

Early one morning, a lone traveler walked down a dusty road. He traveled through a region of what is now Mexico. It was in the days of the Aztec Empire, a long time ago. The traveler wore a serape, a colorful woolen shawl, over his shoulders. It protected him from the chill in the morning air. Soon, he knew, the sun would warm up everything. Then the wide brim of the traveler's straw hat would protect him from the strong rays of the sun.

The road ran through a narrow valley between tall hills. Forests covered the hills' upper slopes, but the lower slopes were bare and brown. In the distance, the traveler could see the snow-capped peak of a tall volcano. He was fascinated by the puff of smoke coming from it.

As the traveler made his way through the valley, he noticed many details. Large boulders lay scattered in the dry grass of nearby fields. Every so often, the traveler passed a small house. It occurred to him that it would be difficult to farm this land. Life must be hard for the people who lived here.

Around a bend in the road, the traveler came upon a young peasant boy. The boy was walking slowly through the field. He seemed to be searching for something. Every now and then he bent down to pick up a stick. The traveler guessed that the boy was gathering firewood. His family would use the firewood to cook their meals.

"Hello, there," the traveler called to the boy.

"Hello," the peasant boy replied, looking up.

The traveler gazed at a small, red adobe hut set back from the road. There was a lemon tree next to the hut. Corn was growing in a field nearby. It was clear that the people who lived there were poor. They must have learned to be quite thrifty in order to live on what little they had.

"Do you live in that house over there?" the traveler asked the boy, pointing to the hut.

"Yes," said the boy. "I live with my mama and papa." The boy stared at the stranger. Strangers seldom passed this way. Still, the man seemed harmless enough, so the boy went back to searching for sticks.

The traveler watched the boy. He knew that the boy's family had to work hard to put food on the table. He looked at the handful of small sticks and twigs the boy was holding.

"I can see that it is not easy to find wood in this field. Why don't you go up into the forest on the hillsides? There must be plenty of wood up there," the traveler said.

"Oh, no!" the peasant boy exclaimed, as though shocked as the suggestion. "That is not possible!"

"Why not?" asked the traveler. "Isn't life hard enough without making it even harder?"

"All of that land in the forest belongs to the emperor," said the boy. "We have heard that he goes hunting there several times a year. The emperor's law says that no one else may enter the forest. If I got caught up there, I would have to pay with my life!" The boy turned away and continued looking for sticks.

"Listen," said the traveler, "there's nobody here now except you and me. You could go into the forest, and no one would find out. I certainly wouldn't tell anyone. You wouldn't get into trouble."

"No thanks," the peasant boy said. "I'll just collect the sticks I can find in this field." He wondered why the stranger would suggest such a roguish idea.

"What a shame," the traveler said. "All that good wood up there going to waste. Your emperor must be a selfish ruler to be unwilling to share his wood." He shook his head, as if to show that such behavior was hard to understand.

The peasant boy looked at the man's face. He thought he saw a rascally look in the man's eyes. The boy did not wish to hear any more daring ideas. He said, "The emperor may not be a generous person, but that doesn't mean I should break the law. My mother always says, 'Two wrongs don't make a right.'"

The traveler shrugged. He said, "Well, have it your way." He turned and looked down the road toward the distant volcano.

"Now," he went on, "I must be on my way. I have a long way to go before dark. Good luck, young man."

The peasant boy said good-bye to the stranger and went back to collecting wood. By late afternoon, he had gathered a large bundle. If they were thrifty with the wood, his family would have enough for a week.

Several days later, another stranger arrived at the red adobe hut. He said he was a messenger from the emperor. The boy and his family were ordered to leave the next morning and return with the stranger to the emperor's palace. They shared their dinner with the messenger. Then they made a space for him to sleep on some blankets on the floor.

The next morning, they all set out for the emperor's palace. The peasant family walked along the road in silence. They were afraid they might be in some kind of trouble. When they arrived at the palace, they were led into the royal throne room. The emperor was sitting on his throne, waiting for them.

The peasant boy looked around the throne room, fascinated by everything he saw. Then he looked at the emperor, who was dressed in his royal garments. When he saw the emperor's face, his eyes grew wide and his jaw dropped. He recognized the man with the rascally look in his eyes!

"You're the stranger," the boy gasped, "the man on the road!" He paused to catch his breath. "You told me to steal the wood from the emperor's forest!" A wave of fear swept over him.

The emperor smiled at the boy and his family.
"There is nothing to be afraid of," he said.
"I often disguise myself and wander about the
empire alone. This way I learn about my subjects.
I can find out whether there are any problems. I
learn whether there is anything I can do to help
my people."

Looking directly at the boy, the emperor went
on, "I am proud to have such honest and loyal
subjects. You refused to break my laws. For that, I
intend to reward you and your family. This chest
of gold is yours."

The peasant boy and his parents were about to thank their emperor for his generous gift, but the emperor stopped them. "There is one more thing," he said. "Thanks to you, I have learned that one of my laws is unjust. From now on, all who wish to enter my forests may do so. Now I invite you all to dine with your emperor. Tonight you will stay in the palace as royal guests!"